The Boy Who Cried Wolf

Edited by: Bob Williams

Once there was a shepherd boy who had to look after a flock of sheep every day.

One day, he felt very lonely and bored. He decided to play a trick on the villagers.

He ran into the village, shouting very loudly, "Help! Help! Wolf! Wolf!"

The villagers heard his cries
and came running to chase away
the wolf.

When they reached the meadow, they asked the boy, "Where is the wolf?"

The shepherd boy said, "Oh! It was here, but now it must have run away."

The villagers talked to him for a while and told him to be careful. Then they left.

The next day, he played the same trick again. He shouted, "Help! Wolf!"

The villagers ran to help the boy. But once again, they did not find any sign of a wolf.

This time, the men were not sure that the boy was telling the truth. The boy just laughed at them.

A few days later, the shepherd boy was once again shouting, "Help! Help! Wolf! Wolf!"

The villagers laughed and said to each other, "He's trying to trick us again!"

But this time a wolf really was chasing the sheep! And no one came to help the boy.

Later, the villagers came by and found many dead sheep. The boy was now very sorry for what he did.

Key Words:

shepherd boy   wolf

sheep   chase

villagers   meadow

village   laughed

shouting   dead

Moral: *People that often tell lies are not trusted even when they tell the truth.*